THE FIFTH

Garfield (Noel)

TREASURY

To Na

From All 'THE LADS' in The "BORED"

BY: JIM DAVIS

Ronan

Liam

Ronnie O'Connor

RAVETTE BOOKS

This edition first published by Ravette Books Limited 1990.

Printed and bound for Ravette Books Limited,
3 Glenside Estate, Star Road,
Partridge Green, Nr. Horsham,
West Sussex RH13 8RA
by Mateu Cromo Artes Gráfica, s.a.

ISBN: 1 85304 321 4

THE FIFTH

Garfield

TREASURY

BY: JIM DAVIS

RAVETTE BOOKS

This edition first published by Ravette Books Limited 1990.

Printed and bound for Ravette Books Limited,
3 Glenside Estate, Star Road,
Partridge Green, Nr. Horsham,
West Sussex RH13 8RA
by Mateu Cromo Artes Gráfica, s.a.

ISBN: 1 85304 321 4

© 1987 United Feature Syndicate, Inc.

JON!

JON! WAKE UP! I'M HAVING NIGHTMARES!

GARFIELD, IF YOU DIDN'T STUFF YOURSELF RIGHT BEFORE GOING TO BED, YOU WOULDN'T DREAM ABOUT BIG, UGLY MONSTERS

DID YOU HEAR WHAT HE CALLED YOU GUYS?

JIM DAVIS 1-11

I THINK I'LL POLISH OFF THAT PEPPERONI PIZZA NOW

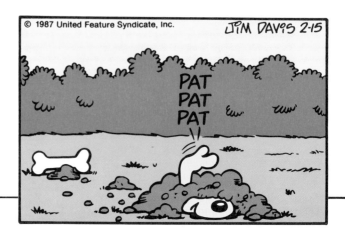

© 1987 United Feature Syndicate, Inc.

JIM DAVIS 5-31

© 1987 United Feature Syndicate, Inc.

© 1987 United Feature Syndicate, Inc.

JIM DAVIS 7-12

© 1987 United Feature Syndicate, Inc.

© 1987 United Feature Syndicate, Inc.

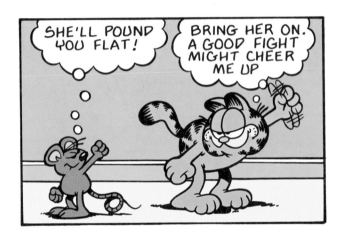

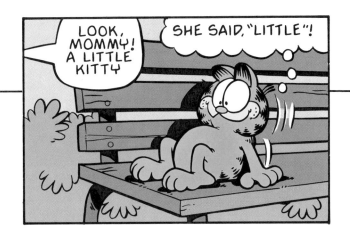

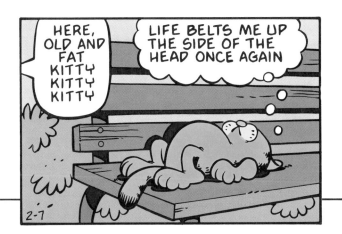

© 1988 United Feature Syndicate, Inc.

CLICK!

THAT'S IT! I'M TIRED OF LIVING WITH YOU BOZOS!

I'M MOVING OUT AND TAKING MY STUFF WITH ME

HOW'S APARTMENT LIFE, GARFIELD?

WITH THE EXCEPTION OF ONE NOSY NEIGHBOR, NOT BAD

JIM DAVIS 5-15

HAPPY 10TH BIRTHDAY, BUDDY. JIM DAVIS

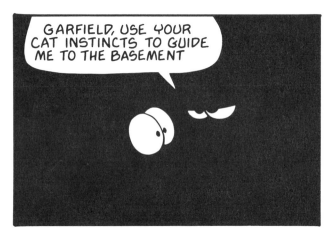

TELL YOU WHAT, GARFIELD. IF I GIVE YOU ONE OF MY HAMBURGERS, WILL YOU STOP STARING AT ME?

AGREED!

JIM DAVIS 8-14

JIM DAVIS 9-4

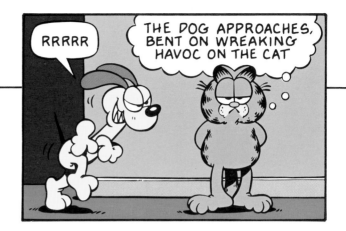

© 1988 United Feature Syndicate, Inc.

Other Garfield books published by Ravette

The Second Garfield Treasury	£5.95
The Third Garfield Treasury	£5.95
The Fourth Garfield Treasury	£5.95

Garfield TV Specials

Here Comes Garfield	£2.95
Garfield On The Town	£2.95
Garfield In The Rough	£2.95
Garfield in Disguise	£2.95
Garfield in Paradise	£2.95
Garfield Goes To Hollywood	£2.95
A Garfield Christmas	£2.95
Garfield's Thanksgiving	£2.95

Garfield Landscapes

Garfield The All-Round Sports Star	£2.95
Garfield The Irresistible	£2.95
Garfield On Vacation	£2.95
Garfield Weighs In!	£2.95
Garfield I Hate Monday	£2.95
Garfield Special Delivery	£2.95
Garfield The Incurable Romantic	£2.95
Garfield Another Serve	£2.95
Garfield Wraps It Up	£2.95
Garfield This Is Your Life	£2.95
Garfield Sheer Genius	£2.95
Garfield Goes Wild	£2.95
Garfield Rebel Without A Clue!	£2.95

Garfield Pocket books

No. 1 Garfield The Great Lover	£1.95
No. 2 Garfield Why Do You Hate Mondays?	£2.50
No. 3 Garfield Does Pooky Need You?	£2.50
No. 4 Garfield Admit It, Odie's OK!	£2.50
No. 5 Garfield Two's Company	£2.50
No. 6 Garfield What's Cooking?	£1.95
No. 7 Garfield Who's Talking?	£1.95
No. 8 Garfield Strikes Again	£1.95
No. 9 Garfield Here's Looking At You	£1.95
No. 10 Garfield We Love You Too	£1.95
No. 11 Garfield Here We Go Again	£1.95
No. 12 Garfield Life and Lasagne	£1.95
No. 13 Garfield In The Pink	£2.50
No. 14 Garfield Just Good Friends	£1.95
No. 15 Garfield Plays It Again	£2.50
No. 16 Garfield Flying High	£2.50
No. 17 Garfield On Top Of The World	£2.50
No. 18 Garfield Happy Landings	£1.95
No. 19 Garfield Going Places	£2.50
No. 20 Garfield Le Magnifique!	£2.50

Garfield A Weekend Away	£4.95
Garfield Book of Cat Names	£2.50
Garfield Best Ever	£4.95
Garfield Selection	£5.95
Garfield How To Party	£3.95
Garfield Easter Bunny	£3.95
Garfield His 9 Lives	£5.95

All these books are available at your local bookshop or newsagent, or can be ordered direct from the publisher. Just tick the titles you require and fill in the form below. Prices and availability subject to change without notice.

Ravette Books Limited, 3 Glenside Estate, Star Road, Partridge Green, Nr. Horsham, West Sussex RH13 8RA

Please send a cheque or postal order and allow the following for postage and packing. UK: Pocket books and TV Specials – 45p for one book plus 20p for the second book and 15p for each additional book. Landscape Series – 45p for one book plus 30p for each additional book. Other titles – 85p for one book plus 60p for each additional book.

Name ....

Address ....

....